Ultimate Keto

Diet Cookbook

The Ultimate Cookbook with Best

Delicious Ketogenic Diet Recipes for

Improve Your Well-Being and Your

Body

Tanya Scofield

Table of Contents

copy and is only allowed with the express written consent from the Publisher. All additional right reserved.

The information in the following pages is broadly considered a truthful and accurate account of facts and as such, any inattention, use, or misuse of the information in question by the reader will render any resulting actions solely under their purview. There are no scenarios in which the publisher or the original author of this work can be in any fashion deemed liable for any hardship or damages that may befall them after undertaking information described herein.

Additionally, the information in the following pages is intended only for informational purposes and should thus be thought of as universal. As befitting its nature, it is presented without assurance regarding its prolonged validity or interim quality. Trademarks that are mentioned are done without written consent and can in no way be considered an endorsement from the trademark holder.

INTRODUCTION

So the Ketogenic Diet is all about reducing the amount of carbohydrates you eat. Does this mean you won't get the kind of energy you need for the day? Of course not! It only means that now, your body has to find other possible sources of energy. Do you know where they will be getting that energy? Even before we talk about how to do keto – it's important to first consider why this particular diet works. What actually happens to your body to make you lose weight? As you probably know, the body uses food as an energy source. Everything you eat is turned into energy, so that you can get up and do whatever you need to accomplish for the day. The main energy source is sugar so what happens is that you eat something, the body breaks it down into sugar, and the sugar is processed into energy. Typically, the "sugar" is taken directly from the food you eat so if you eat just the right amount of food, then your body is fueled for the whole day. If you eat too much, then the sugar is stored in your body – hence the accumulation of fat.

But what happens if you eat less food? This is where the Ketogenic Diet comes in. You see, the process of creating sugar from food is usually faster if the food happens to be rich in carbohydrates. Bread, rice, grain, pasta – all of these are carbohydrates and they're the easiest food types to turn into energy.

So here's the situation – you are eating less carbohydrates every day. To keep you energetic, the body breaks down the stored fat and turns them into molecules called ketone bodies. The process of turning the fat into ketone bodies is called "Ketosis" and obviously – this is where the name of the Ketogenic Diet comes from. The ketone bodies take the place of glucose in keeping you energetic. As long as you keep your carbohydrates reduced, the body will keep getting its energy from your body fat.

The Ketogenic Diet is often praised for its simplicity and when you look at it properly, the process is really straightforward. The Science behind the effectivity of the diet is also well-documented, and has been proven multiple times by different medical fields. For example, an article on Diet Review by Harvard provided a lengthy discussion on how the Ketogenic Diet works and why it is so effective for those who choose to use this diet.

But Fat Is the Enemy...Or Is It?

No – fat is NOT the enemy. Unfortunately, years of bad science told us that fat is something you have to avoid – but it's actually a very helpful thing for weight loss! Even before we move forward with this book, we'll have to discuss exactly what "healthy fats" are, and why they're actually the good guys. To do this, we need to make a distinction between the different kinds of fat. You've probably heard of them before and it is a little bit confusing at first. We'll try to go through them as simply as possible:

Saturated fat. This is the kind you want to avoid. They're also called "solid fat" because each molecule is packed with hydrogen atoms. Simply put, it's the kind of fat that can easily cause a blockage in your body. It can raise cholesterol levels and lead to heart problems or a stroke. Saturated fat is something you can find in meat, dairy products, and other processed food items. Now, you're probably wondering: isn't the Ketogenic Diet packed with saturated fat? The answer is: not necessarily. You'll find later in the recipes given that the Ketogenic Diet promotes primarily unsaturated fat or healthy fat. While there are definitely many meat recipes in the list, most of these recipes contain healthy fat sources.

Unsaturated Fat. These are the ones dubbed as healthy fat. They're the kind of fat you find in avocado, nuts, and other ingredients you usually find in Keto-friendly recipes. They're known to lower blood cholesterol and actually come in two types: polyunsaturated and monounsaturated. Both are good for your body but the benefits slightly vary, depending on what you're consuming.

Chicken Salad

Preparation Time: 15 minutes

Cooking Time: 25 minutes

Servings: 4

Ingredients:

- For the Buffalo chicken salad:
- 2 chicken breasts (225 g) peeled, boned, cut in half
- 2 tablespoons of hot cayenne pepper sauce (or another type of hot sauce), plus an addition depending on taste
- 2 tablespoons of olive oil
- 2 romaine lettuce heart, cut into 2 cm strips
- 4 celery stalks, finely sliced
- 2 carrots, roughly grated
- 2 fresh onions, only the green part, sliced
- 125 ml of blue cheese dressing, recipe to follow
- For the seasoning of blue cheese
- 2 tablespoons mayonnaise
- 70 ml of partially skimmed buttermilk
- 70 ml low-fat white yoghurt
- 1 tablespoon of wine vinegar

- ½ teaspoon of sugar
- 35 g of chopped blue cheese
- Salt and freshly ground black pepper

Directions:

1. For the Buffalo chicken salad:
2. Preheat the grid.
3. Place the chicken between 2 sheets of baking paper and beat it with a meat tenderizer so that it is about 2 cm thick, then cut the chicken sideways creating 1 cm strips.
4. In a large bowl, add the hot sauce and oil, add the chicken and turn it over until it is well soaked. Place the chicken on a baking tray and grill until well cooked, about 4-6 minutes, turning it once.
5. In a large bowl, add the lettuce, celery, grated carrots and fresh onions. Add the seasoning of blue cheese. Distribute the vegetables in 4 plates and arrange the chicken on each of the dishes. Serve with hot sauce on the side.
6. For the blue cheese dressing:
7. Cover a small bowl with absorbent paper folded in four. Spread the yoghurt on the paper and put it in the fridge for 20 minutes to drain and firm it.

8. In a medium bowl, beat the buttermilk and firm yogurt with mayonnaise until well blended. Add the vinegar and sugar and keep beating until well blended. Add the blue cheese and season with salt and pepper to taste.

Nutrition: 321 calories Fat 3 Fiber 5 Carbs 7 Protein 4

Avocado and Kale Eggs

Preparation Time: 10 minutes

Cooking time: 30 minutes

Servings: 3

Ingredients:

- 1 teaspoon ghee
- 1 red onion, sliced
- 4 oz. chorizo, sliced into thin rounds
- 1 cup chopped kale
- 1 ripe avocado, pitted, peeled, chopped
- 4 eggs
- Salt and black pepper to season

Directions:

1. Preheat oven to 370ºF.

2. Melt ghee in a cast iron pan over medium heat and sauté the onion for 2 minutes. Add the chorizo and cook for 2 minutes more, flipping once.

3. Introduce the kale in batches with a splash of water to wilt, season lightly with salt, stir and

cook for 3 minutes. Mix in the avocado and turn the heat off.

4. Create four holes in the mixture, crack the eggs into each hole, sprinkle with salt and black pepper, and slide the pan into the preheated oven to bake for 6 minutes until the egg whites are set or firm and yolks still runny. Season to taste with salt and pepper, and serve right away with low carb toasts.

Nutrition: Kcal 274, Fat 23g, Net Carbs 4g, Protein 13g

Tofu Meat and Salad

Preparation Time: 15 minutes

Cooking Time: 20 minutes

Servings: 3

Ingredients:

- 1 tablespoon of garlic sauce and chili in a bottle
- 1 1/2 tablespoon sesame oil
- 3 tablespoons of low-sodium soy sauce
- 60 ml hoisin sauce
- 2 tablespoons rice vinegar
- 2 tablespoons of sherry or Chinese cooking wine
- 225 g of extra-solid tofu
- 2 teaspoons of rapeseed oil
- 2 tablespoons of finely chopped fresh ginger
- 4 spring onions, with the green part chopped and set aside, in thin slices
- 225 g of minced lean beef (90% or more lean)
- 25 g of diced Chinese water chestnuts
- 1 large head of cappuccino lettuce, with the leaves separated, but without the outer ones
- 1 red pepper, diced

Directions:

- In a bowl, mix together the garlic and chili sauce, sesame oil, soy sauce, hoisin sauce, vinegar and sherry.
- Cut the tofu into 1 cm thick slices and place them on a kitchen towel. Use the cloth to dab the tofu well to remove as much water as possible. Should take a couple of minutes and about three dish towels. Chop the dry tofu well and set aside.
- Heat the oil in a wok or in a very large pan and medium flame. Add the ginger and the white part of the spring onions and cook until the spring onions become translucent and the ginger fragrant, for about 2-3 minutes. Add the beef and tofu and cook, stirring, until the meat becomes dull and freshly cooked, for about 4-5 minutes. Add the sauce set aside. Reduce the flame and simmer slowly, stirring, for another 3-4 minutes. Add the chestnuts and mix well to incorporate.
- Fill each lettuce leaf with stuffing. Serve by decorating with the green part of the spring onions, red pepper and peanuts.

Nutrition: Calories 122 Fat 2 Protein 66

Asparagus and Pistachios Vinaigrette

Preparation Time: 10 minutes

Cooking Time: 5minutes

Servings: 2

Ingredients:

- Two 455g bunches of large asparagus, without the tip
- 1 tablespoon of olive oil
- Salt and freshly ground black pepper
- 6 tablespoons of sliced pistachios blanched and boiled
- 1 1/2 tablespoon lemon juice
- 1/4 teaspoon of sugar
- 1 1/2 teaspoon lemon zest

Directions:

1. Preheat the oven to 220°C. Put the grill in the top third of the oven. Place the asparagus on a baking tray covered with baking paper. Sprinkle with olive oil and season with a little salt and pepper. Bake for 15 minutes, until soft.

2. Meanwhile, blend 5 tablespoons of almonds, lemon juice, sugar and 6 tablespoons of water for 1 minute until smooth. Taste and regulate salt. Pour the sauce on a plate and put the spinach on the sauce. Decorate with peel and the remaining spoon of pistachios

Nutrition: Calories 560 Fat 5 Fiber 2 Carbs 3 Protein 9

DINNER

Beef-Stuffed Mushrooms

Preparation Time: 20 minutes

Cooking Time: 25 minutes

Servings: 4

Ingredients:

- 4 mushrooms, stemmed
- 3 tablespoons olive oil, divided
- 1 yellow onion, sliced thinly
- 1 red bell pepper, sliced into strips
- 1 green bell pepper, sliced into strips
- Salt and pepper to taste
- 8 oz. beef, sliced thinly
- 3 oz. provolone cheese, sliced
- Chopped parsley

Directions:

1. Preheat your oven to 350 degrees F.
2. Arrange the mushrooms on a baking pan.
3. Brush with oil.

4. Add the remaining oil to a pan over medium heat.

5. Cook onion and bell peppers for 5 minutes.

6. Season with salt and pepper.

7. Place onion mixture on a plate.

8. Cook the beef in the pan for 5 minutes.

9. Sprinkle with salt and pepper.

10. Add the onion mixture back to the pan.

11. Mix well.

12. Fill the mushrooms with the beef mixture and cheese.

13. Bake in the oven for 15 minutes.

Nutrition: Calories 333 Total Fat 20.3 g Saturated Fat 6.7 g Cholesterol 61 mg Sodium 378 mg Total Carbohydrate 8.2 g Dietary Fiber 3.7 g Protein 25.2 g Total Sugars 7 g Potassium 789 mg

Rib Roast

Preparation Time: 15 minutes

Cooking Time: 3 hours

Servings: 8

Ingredients:

- 1 rib roast
- Salt to taste
- 12 cloves garlic, chopped
- 2 teaspoons lemon zest
- 6 tablespoons fresh rosemary, chopped
- 5 sprigs thyme

Directions:

1. Preheat your oven to 325 degrees F.
2. Season all sides of rib roast with salt.
3. Place the rib roast in a baking pan.
4. Sprinkle with garlic, lemon zest and rosemary.
5. Add herb sprigs on top.
6. Roast for 3 hours.

Let rest for a few minutes and then slice and serve.

Nutrition: Calories 329 Total Fat 27 g Saturated Fat 9 g Cholesterol 59 mg Sodium 498 mg

Total Carbohydrate 5.3 g Dietary Fiber 1.8 g Protein 18 g Total Sugars 2 gPotassium 493 mg

Beef Stir Fry

Preparation Time: 15 minutes

Cooking Time: 10 minutes

Servings: 4

Ingredients:

- 1 tablespoon soy sauce
- 1 tablespoon ginger, minced
- 1 teaspoon cornstarch
- 1 teaspoon dry sherry
- 12 oz. beef, sliced into strips
- 1 teaspoon toasted sesame oil
- 2 tablespoons oyster sauce
- 1 lb. baby bok choy, sliced
- 3 tablespoons chicken broth

Directions:

1. Mix soy sauce, ginger, cornstarch and dry sherry in a bowl.
2. Toss the beef in the mixture.
3. Pour oil into a pan over medium heat.
4. Cook the beef for 5 minutes, stirring.

5. Add oyster sauce, bok choy and chicken broth to the pan.

6. Cook for 1 minute.

Nutrition: Calories 247 Total Fat 15.8 g Saturated Fat 4 g Cholesterol 69 mg Sodium 569 mg Total Carbohydrate 6.3 g Dietary Fiber 1.1 g Protein 25 g

Sweet & Sour Pork

Preparation Time: 15 minutes

Cooking Time: 15 minutes

Servings: 4

Ingredients:

- 1 lb. pork chops
- Salt and pepper to taste
- ½ cup sesame seeds
- 2 tablespoons peanut oil
- 2 tablespoons soy sauce
- 3 tablespoons apricot jam
- Chopped scallions

Directions:

1. Season pork chops with salt and pepper.
2. Press sesame seeds on both sides of pork.
3. Pour oil into a pan over medium heat.
4. Cook pork for 3 to 5 minutes per side.
5. Transfer to a plate.
6. In a bowl, mix soy sauce and apricot jam.
7. Simmer for 3 minutes.

8. Pour sauce over the pork and garnish with scallions before serving.

Nutrition: Calories 414 Total Fat 27.5 g Saturated Fat 5.6 g Cholesterol 68 mg Sodium 607 mg Total Carbohydrate 12.9 g Dietary Fiber 1.8 g Protein 29 g   Total Sugars 9 g Potassium 332 mg

Grilled Pork with Salsa

Preparation Time: 30 minutes

Cooking Time: 15 minutes

Servings: 4

Ingredients:

- Salsa
- 1 onion, chopped
- 1 tomato, chopped
- 1 peach, chopped
- 1 apricot, chopped
- 1 tablespoon olive oil
- 1 tablespoon lime juice
- 2 tablespoons fresh cilantro, chopped
- Salt and pepper to taste
- Pork
- 1 lb. pork tenderloin, sliced
- 1 tablespoon olive oil
- Salt and pepper to taste
- ½ teaspoon ground cumin
- ¾ teaspoon chili powder

Directions:

1. Combine salsa ingredients in a bowl.

2. Cover and refrigerate.

3. Brush pork tenderloin with oil.

4. Season with salt, pepper, cumin and chili powder.

5. Grill pork for 5 to 7 minutes per side.

6. Slice pork and serve with salsa.

Nutrition: Calories 219 Total Fat 9.5 g Saturated Fat 1.8 g Cholesterol 74 mg Sodium 512 mg Total Carbohydrate 8.3 g Dietary Fiber 1.5 g Protein 24 g Total Sugars 6 gPotassium 600 mg

Garlic Pork Loin

Preparation Time: 15 minutes

Cooking Time: 1 hour

Servings: 6

Ingredients:

- 1 ½ lb. pork loin roast
- 4 cloves garlic, sliced into slivers
- Salt and pepper to taste

Directions:

1. Preheat your oven to 425 degrees F.
2. Make several slits all over the pork roast.
3. Insert garlic slivers.
4. Sprinkle with salt and pepper.
5. Roast in the oven for 1 hour.

Nutrition: Calories 235 Total Fat 13.3 g Saturated Fat 2.6 g Cholesterol 71 mg Sodium 450 mg Total Carbohydrate 1.7 g Dietary Fiber 0.3 g Protein 25.7 g Total Sugars 3 g Potassium 383 mg

Chicken Pesto

Preparation Time: 15 minutes

Cooking Time: 25 minutes

Servings: 4

Ingredients:

- 1 lb. chicken cutlet
- Salt and pepper to taste
- 1 tablespoon olive oil
- ½ cup onion, chopped
- ½ cup heavy cream
- ½ cup dry white wine
- 1 tomato, chopped
- ¼ cup pesto
- 2 tablespoons basil, chopped

Directions:

1. Season chicken with salt and pepper.
2. Pour oil into a pan over medium heat.
3. Cook chicken for 3 to 4 minutes per side.
4. Place the chicken on a plate.
5. Add the onion to the pan.
6. Cook for 1 minute.

7. Stir in the rest of the ingredients.

8. Bring to a boil.

9. Simmer for 15 minutes.

10. Put the chicken back to the pan.

11. Cook for 2 more minutes and then serve.

Nutrition: Calories 371 Total Fat 23.7 g Saturated Fat 9.2 g Cholesterol 117 mg Sodium 361 mg Total Carbohydrate 5.7 g Dietary Fiber 1 g Protein 27.7 g Total Sugars 3 g Potassium 567 mg

Garlic Parmesan Chicken Wings

Preparation Time: 20 minutes

Cooking Time: 20 minutes

Servings: 8

Ingredients:

- Cooking spray
- ½ cup all-purpose flour
- Pepper to taste
- 2 tablespoons garlic powder
- 3 eggs, beaten
- 1 ¼ cups Parmesan cheese, grated
- 2 cups breadcrumbs
- 2 lb. chicken wings

Directions:

1. Preheat your oven to 450 degrees F.
2. Spray baking pan with oil.
3. In a bowl, mix the flour, pepper and garlic powder.
4. Add eggs to another bowl.
5. Mix the Parmesan cheese and breadcrumbs in another bowl.

6. Dip the chicken wings in the first, second and third bowls.

7. Spray chicken wings with oil.

8. Bake in the oven for 20 minutes.

Nutrition: Calories 221 Total Fat 11.6 g Saturated Fat 3.9 g Cholesterol 122 mg Sodium 242 mg Total Carbohydrate 8 g Dietary Fiber 0.4 g Protein 16 g Total Sugars 3 g Potassium 163 mg

Crispy Baked Shrimp

Preparation Time: 15 minutes

Cooking Time: 10 minutes

Servings: 4

Ingredients:

- ¼ cup whole-wheat breadcrumbs
- 3 tablespoons olive oil, divided
- 1 ½ lb. jumbo shrimp, peeled and deveined
- Salt and pepper to taste
- 2 tablespoons lemon juice
- 1 tablespoon garlic, chopped
- 2 tablespoons butter
- ¼ cup Parmesan cheese, grated
- 2 tablespoons chives, chopped

Directions:

1. Preheat your oven to 425 degrees F.
2. Add breadcrumbs to a pan over medium heat.
3. Cook until toasted.
4. Transfer to a plate.
5. Coat baking pan with 1 tablespoon oil.
6. Arrange shrimp in a single layer in a baking pan.

---

7. Season with salt and pepper.

8. Mix lemon juice, garlic and butter in a bowl.

9. Pour mixture on top of the shrimp.

10. Add Parmesan cheese and chives to the breadcrumbs.

11. Sprinkle breadcrumbs on top of the shrimp.

12. Bake for 10 minutes.

Nutrition: Calories 340 Total Fat 18.7 g Saturated Fat 6 g Cholesterol 293 mg Sodium 374 mg Total Carbohydrate 6 g Dietary Fiber 0.8 g Protein 36.9 g Total Sugars 2 g Potassium 483 mg

Herbed Mediterranean Fish Fillet

Preparation Time: 20 minutes

Cooking Time: 1 hour

Servings: 6

Ingredients:

- 3 lb. sea bass fillet
- Salt to taste
- 2 tablespoons tarragon, chopped
- ¼ cup dry white wine
- 3 tablespoons olive oil, divided
- 1 tablespoon butter
- 2 cloves garlic, minced
- 2 cups whole-wheat breadcrumbs
- 3 tablespoons parsley, chopped
- 3 tablespoons oregano, chopped
- 3 tablespoons fresh basil, chopped

Directions:

1. Preheat your oven to 350 degrees F.
2. Season fish with salt and tarragon.
3. Pour half of oil into a roasting pan.
4. Stir in wine.
5. Add the fish in the roasting pan.

6. Bake in the oven for 50 minutes.

7. Add remaining oil to a pan over medium heat.

8. Cook herbs, breadcrumbs and salt.

9. Spread breadcrumb mixture on top of fish and bake for 5 minutes.

Nutrition: Calories 288 Total Fat 12.7 g Saturated Fat 2.9 g Cholesterol 65 mg Sodium 499 mg

Total Carbohydrate 10.4 g Dietary Fiber 1.8 g

Protein 29.5 g Total Sugars 1 g Potassium 401 mg

Mushroom Stuffed with Ricotta

Preparation Time: 10 minutes

Cooking Time: 10 minutes

Servings: 4

Ingredients:

- 4 large mushrooms, stemmed
- 1 tablespoon olive oil
- Salt and pepper to taste
- ¼ cup basil, chopped
- 1 cup ricotta cheese
- ¼ cup Parmesan cheese, grated

Directions:

1. Preheat your grill.
2. Coat the mushrooms with oil.
3. Season with salt and pepper.
4. Grill for 5 minutes.
5. Stuff each mushroom with a mixture of basil, ricotta cheese and Parmesan cheese.
6. Grill for another 5 minutes.

Nutrition: Calories 259 Total Fat 17.3 g Saturated Fat 5.4 gCholesterol 24 mg Sodium 509 mg

Total Carbohydrate 14.9 g Dietary Fiber 2.6 g Protein 12.2 g Total Sugars 7 g Potassium 572 mg

Thai Chopped Salad

Preparation Time: 15 minutes

Cooking Time: 0 minutes

Servings: 4

Ingredients:

- 10 oz. kale and cabbage mix
- 14 oz. tofu, sliced into cubes and fried crispy
- ½ cup vinaigrette

Directions:

1. Arrange kale and cabbage in a serving platter.
2. Top with the tofu cubes.
3. Drizzle with the vinaigrette.

Nutrition: Calories 332 Total Fat 15 g Saturated Fat 1.5 g Cholesterol 0 mg Sodium 236 mg Total Carbohydrate 26.3 g Dietary Fiber 7.6 g Protein 1.3 g Total Sugars 13 g Potassium 41 mg

Lemon & Rosemary Salmon

Preparation Time: 10 minutes

Cooking Time: 15 minutes

Servings: 4

Ingredients:

- 4 salmon fillets
- Salt and pepper to taste
- 4 tablespoons butter
- 1 lemon, sliced
- 8 rosemary sprigs

Directions:

1. Season salmon with salt and pepper.
2. Place salmon on a foil sheet.
3. Top with butter, lemon slices and rosemary sprigs.
4. Fold the foil and seal.
5. Bake in the oven at 450 degrees F for 15 minutes.

Nutrition: Calories 365 Total Fat 22 g Saturated Fat 6 g Cholesterol 86 mg Sodium 445 mg Total Carbohydrate 5 g Dietary Fiber 1.9 g Protein 29.8 g Total Sugars 3 g Potassium 782 mg

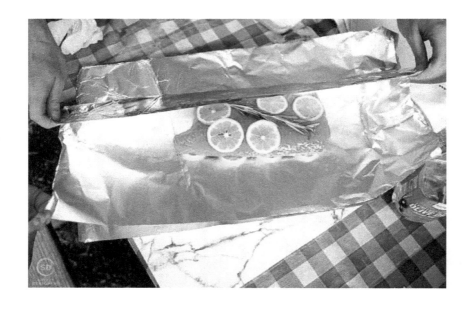

Chicken Kurma

Preparation Time: 20 minutes

Cooking Time: 25 minutes

Servings: 6

Ingredients:

- 1 tablespoon olive oil
- 1 onion, diced
- 3 cloves garlic, sliced thinly
- 1 ginger, minced
- 2 tomatoes, diced
- 1 serrano pepper, minced
- Salt and pepper to taste
- 1 teaspoon ground turmeric
- 1 tablespoon tomato paste
- 1 ½ lb. chicken, sliced
- 1 red bell pepper, chopped

Directions:

1. Pour oil into a pan over medium heat.
2. Cook onion for 3 minutes.
3. Add garlic, ginger, tomatoes, Serrano pepper, salt, pepper, and turmeric and tomato paste.

---

4. Bring to a boil.

5. Reduce heat and simmer for 10 minutes.

6. Add chicken and cook for 5 minutes.

7. Stir in red bell pepper.

8. Cook for 5 minutes.

Nutrition: Calories 175 Total Fat 15.2 g Saturated Fat 3 g Cholesterol 115 mg Sodium 400 mg Total Carbohydrate 7 g Dietary Fiber 1.8 g Protein 24 g Total Sugars 3 g Potassium 436 mg

Pork Chops with Bacon & Mushrooms

Preparation Time: 10 minutes

Cooking Time: 20 minutes

Servings: 4

Ingredients:

- 6 strips bacon, chopped
- 4 pork chops
- Salt and pepper to taste
- 2 cloves garlic, minced
- 8 oz. mushrooms, sliced
- 1 tablespoon olive oil
- 5 sprigs fresh thyme
- 2/3 cup chicken broth
- 1/2 cup heavy cream

Directions:

1. Cook bacon in a pan until crispy.
2. Transfer bacon on a plate.
3. Sprinkle salt and pepper on the pork chops.
4. Cook the pork chops in bacon fat for 4 minutes per side.

---

5. Transfer pork chops on a plate.

6. Add the garlic and mushrooms in the pan.

7. Add the olive oil

8. Cook for 5 minutes.

9. Pour in the broth and let the mixture boil.

10. Stir in the heavy cream and reduce the heat to low.

11. Put the bacon and pork chops back to the pan.

12. Cook for 3 more minutes before serving.

Nutrition: Calories 516 Total Fat 41.3g Saturated Fat 15.4g Cholesterol 121mg Sodium 851mg Total Carbohydrate 4.2g Dietary Fiber 1.1g Total Sugars 1.2g Protein 31.7g Potassium 679mg

Pork

Preparation Time: 10 minutes

Cooking Time: 20 minutes

Servings: 4

Ingredients:

- A single pound of pork tenderloin
- A quarter cup of oil
- 3 medium shallots (chop them finely)

Directions:

1. Slice your pork into thick slices (go for about a half-inch thick).
2. Chop up your shallots before placing them on a plate.
3. Get a cast-iron skillet and warm up the oil
4. Press your pork into your shallots on both sides. Press firmly to make sure that they stick.
5. Place the slices of pork with shallots into the warm oil and then cook until it's done. The shallots may burn, but they will still be fine.
6. Make sure the pork is cooked through thoroughly.

Nutrition: Calories-519 Fat-36   grams Protein-46 grams Carbs-7 grams

Garlic Shrimp

Preparation Time: 10 minutes

Cooking Time: 30 minutes

Servings: 4

Ingredients:

- 2 minced garlic cloves
- 2 whole garlic cloves
- The juice from half a lemon
- 2 tablespoons of oil (olive)
- 2 tablespoons of butter
- ¾ pounds of either small or medium shrimp (it needs to be both shelled and deveined)
- A quarter of a teaspoon of paprika
- A quarter of a teaspoon of pepper flakes (red ones)
- 2 tablespoons of parsley that is chopped.

Directions:

1. Sprinkle your shrimp with a teaspoon of salt (fine grain sea salt) and let it sit for ten minutes.
2. Get a skillet.

3. Heat the butter with olive oil over a heat that is medium-high.

4. Add the flakes and garlic.

5. Sauté for half a minute.

6. Add your shrimp and cook until they have turned pink. This will take approximately two minutes. Stir constantly.

7. Add paprika and juice from the lemon.

8. Cook for another sixty seconds.

Nutrition Per serving Calories-260 Fat-18 grams Carbs-none Protein-24 protein

Pork Chop

Preparation Time: 10 minutes

Cooking Time: 30 minutes

Servings: 2

Ingredients:

- A dozen pork chop (boneless and thin cut)
- 2 cups of spinach (you should use baby spinach for this)
- 4 cloves of garlic
- A dozen slices provolone cheese

Directions:

1. Preheat your oven to a temperature of 350.
2. Press the garlic cloves using a garlic press. The cloves should go through the press and into a small bowl.
3. Spread the garlic that you have made onto one side of the pork chops.
4. Flip half a dozen chops while making sure the garlic side is down.
5. You should do this on a baking sheet that is rimmed.

6. Divide your spinach between the half dozen chops.

7. Fold cheese slices in half.

8. Put them on top of the spinach.

9. Put a second pork chop on top of the first set, but this time make sure that the garlic side is up.

10. Bake for 20 minutes.

11. Cover each chop with another piece of cheese.

12. Bake another 15 minutes.

13. Your meat meter should be at 160 degrees when you check with a thermometer.

Nutrition: Calories-436 Fat-25   grams Carbs-2 grams Protein-47 grams

Citrus Egg Salad

Preparation Time: 10 minutes

Cooking Time: 20 minutes

Servings: 3

Ingredients:

- Half a dozen eggs (6)
- A single teaspoon of mustard (go with Dijon)
- 2 tablespoons of mayo
- A single teaspoon of lemon juice

Directions:

1. Place the eggs gently in a medium saucepan.
2. Add cold water until your eggs are covered by an inch.
3. Bring to a boil.
4. You should do this for ten minutes. Remove from your heat and cool. Peel your eggs under running water that is cold.
5. Put your eggs in a food processor. Pulse until they are chopped.
6. Stir in condiments and juice.

Nutrition: Calories-222 Fat-19 grams Protein-13 grams Carbs-1 gram

Chowder

Preparation Time: 10 minutes

Cooking Time: 30 minutes

Servings: 4

Ingredients:

- A single tablespoon of butter
- 5 minced garlic cloves
- An entire head of cauliflower (cut it into florets that are small)
- Half of a teaspoon of oregano (use dried)
- Half a cup of carrots that have been diced
- Half a cup of onions that have been diced
- A cup and a half of broth (use vegetable)
- A quarter cup of cream cheese

Directions:

1. Get a soup pot.
2. Heat your butter.
3. Add garlic and onions.

4. Sauté for a few moments.

5. Add the rest of the ingredients to the pot.

6. Bring to a boil.

7. Slow the heat and put it on a simmer.

8. Cook for 15 minutes.

9. Shut off the flame.

10. Use a hand blender to blend the soup partly in the pot.

11. Switch the flame back on.

12. Add a cup of broth.

13. Add the cream cheese.

14. Simmer for 10 minutes and switch off the flame again.

Nutrition: Calories-143 Fat-8.4 grams Carbs-15.2 grams Protein-4.5 grams

Bulgur Appetizer Salad

Preparation Time: 30 minutes

Cooking Time: 0 minutes

Servings: 4

Ingredients:

- 1 cup bulgur
- 2 cups hot water
- Black pepper to the taste
- 2 cups corn
- 1 cucumber, chopped
- 2 tablespoons lemon juice
- 2 tablespoons balsamic vinegar
- ¼ cup olive oil

Directions:

1. In a bowl, mix bulgur with the water, cover, leave aside for 30 minutes, fluff with a fork and transfer to a salad bowl.
2. Add corn, cucumber, oil with lemon juice, vinegar and pepper, toss, divide into small cups and serve.

Nutrition: Calories 130 Fat 2 Fiber 2 Carbs 7 Protein 6

Cocoa Bars

Preparation Time: 2 hours

Cooking Time: 0 minutes

Servings: 12

Ingredients:

- 1 cup unsweetened cocoa chips
- 2 cups rolled oats
- 1 cup low-fat peanut butter
- ½ cup chia seeds
- ½ cup raisins
- ¼ cup coconut sugar
- ½ cup coconut milk

Directions:

1. Put 1 and ½ cups oats in your blender, pulse well, transfer this to a bowl, add the rest of the oats, cocoa chips, chia seeds, raisins, sugar and milk, stir really well, spread this into a square pan,

press well, keep in the fridge for 2 hours, slice into 12 bars and serve.

Nutrition: Calories 198 Fat 5 Fiber 4 Carbs 10 Protein 89

Cinnamon Apple Chips

Preparation Time: 10 minutes

Cooking Time: 2 hours

Servings: 4

Ingredients:

- Cooking spray
- 2 teaspoons cinnamon powder
- 2 apples, cored and thinly sliced

Directions:

1. Arrange apple slices on a lined baking sheet, spray them with cooking oil, sprinkle cinnamon, introduce in the oven and bake at 300 degrees F for 2 hours.

2. Divide into bowls and serve as a snack.

Nutrition: Calories 80 Fat 0 Fiber 3 Carbs 7 Protein 4

Greek Party Dip

Preparation Time: 10 minutes

Cooking Time: 0 minutes

Servings: 4

Ingredients:

- ½ cup coconut cream
- 1 cup fat-free Greek yogurt
- 2 teaspoons dill, dried
- 2 teaspoons thyme, dried
- 1 teaspoon sweet paprika
- 2 teaspoons no-salt-added sun-dried tomatoes, chopped
- 2 teaspoons parsley, chopped
- 2 teaspoons chives, chopped
- Black pepper to the taste

Directions:

1. In a bowl, mix cream with yogurt, dill with thyme, paprika, tomatoes, parsley, chives and pepper, stir well, divide into smaller bowls and serve as a dip.

Nutrition: Calories 100 Fat 1 Fiber 4 Carbs 8 Protein 3

Spicy Pumpkin Seeds Bowls

Preparation Time: 10 minutes

Cooking Time: 20 minutes

Servings: 6

Ingredients:

- ½ tablespoon chili powder
- ½ teaspoon cayenne pepper
- 2 cups pumpkin seeds
- 2 teaspoons lime juice

Directions:

1. Spread pumpkin seeds on a lined baking sheet, add lime juice, cayenne and chili powder, toss well, introduce in the oven, roast at 275 degrees F for 20 minutes, divide into small bowls and serve as a snack.

Nutrition: Calories 170 Fat 2 Fiber 7 Carbs 12 Protein 6

Apple and Pecans Bowls

Preparation Time: 10 minutes

Cooking Time: 0 minutes

Servings: 4

Ingredients:

- 4 big apples, cored, peeled and cubed
- 2 teaspoons lemon juice
- ¼ cup pecans, chopped

Directions:

1. In a bowl, mix apples with lemon juice and pecans, toss, divide into small bowls and serve as a snack.

Nutrition: Calories 120 Fat 4 Fiber 3 Carbs 12 Protein 3

Shrimp Muffins

Preparation Time: 10 minutes

Cooking Time: 45 minutes

Servings: 6

Ingredients:

- 1 spaghetti squash, peeled and halved
- 2 tablespoons avocado mayonnaise
- 1 cup low-fat mozzarella cheese, shredded
- 8 ounces' shrimp, peeled, cooked and chopped
- 1 and ½ cups almond flour
- 1 teaspoon parsley, dried
- 1 garlic clove, minced
- Black pepper to the taste
- Cooking spray

Directions:

1. Arrange the squash on a lined baking sheet, introduce in the oven at 375 degrees F, bake for 30 minutes, scrape flesh into a bowl, add pepper, parsley flakes, flour, shrimp, mayo and mozzarella and stir well, divide this mix into a muffin tray greased with cooking spray, bake in

the oven at 375 degrees F for 15 minutes and serve them cold as a snack.

Nutrition: Calories 140 Fat 2 Fiber 4 Carbs 14 Protein 12

Zucchini Bowls

Preparation Time: 10 minutes

Cooking Time: 20 minutes

Servings: 12

Ingredients:

- Cooking spray
- ½ cup dill, chopped
- 1 egg
- ½ cup whole wheat flour
- Black pepper to the taste
- 1 yellow onion, chopped
- 2 garlic cloves, minced
- 3 zucchinis, grated

Directions:

1. In a bowl, mix zucchinis with garlic, onion, flour, pepper, egg and dill, stir well, shape small bowls out of this mix, arrange them on a lined baking sheet, grease them with some cooking spray, bake at 400 degrees F for 20 minutes, flipping them halfway, divide them into bowls and serve as a snack.

Nutrition: Calories 120, Fat 1 Fiber 4 Carbs 12 Protein 6

Cheesy Mushrooms Caps

Preparation Time: 10 minutes

Cooking Time: 30 minutes

Servings: 20

Ingredients:

- 20 white mushroom caps
- 1 garlic clove, minced
- 3 tablespoons parsley, chopped
- 2 yellow onions, chopped
- Black pepper to the taste
- ½ cup low-fat parmesan, grated
- ¼ cup low-fat mozzarella, grated
- A drizzle of olive oil
- 2 tablespoons non-fat yogurt

Directions:

1. Heat up a pan with some oil over medium heat, add garlic and onion, stir, cook for 10 minutes and transfer to a bowl.

2. Add black pepper, garlic, parsley, mozzarella, parmesan and yogurt, stir well, stuff the mushroom caps with this mix, arrange them on a

lined baking sheet, bake in the oven at 400 degrees F for 20 minutes and serve them as an appetizer.

Nutrition: Calories 120, Fat 1 Fiber 3 Carbs 11 Protein 7

Mozzarella Cauliflower Bars

Preparation Time: 10 minutes

Cooking Time: 40 minutes

Servings: 12

Ingredients:

- 1 big cauliflower head, riced
- ½ cup low-fat mozzarella cheese, shredded
- ¼ cup egg whites
- 1 teaspoon Italian seasoning
- Black pepper to the taste

Directions:

1. Spread the cauliflower rice on a lined baking sheet, cook in the oven at 375 degrees F for 20 minutes, transfer to a bowl, add black pepper, cheese, seasoning and egg whites, stir well, spread into a rectangle pan and press well on the bottom.
2. Introduce in the oven at 375 degrees F, bake for 20 minutes, cut into 12 bars and serve as a snack.

Nutrition: Calories 140 Fat 1 Fiber 3 Carbs 6 Protein 6

Shrimp and Pineapple Salsa

Preparation Time: 10 minutes

Cooking Time: 40 minutes

Servings: 4

Ingredients:

- 1-pound large shrimp, peeled and deveined
- 20 ounces canned pineapple chunks
- 1 tablespoon garlic powder
- 1 cup red bell peppers, chopped
- Black pepper to the taste

Directions:

1. Place shrimp in a baking dish, add pineapple, garlic, bell peppers and black pepper, toss a bit, introduce in the oven, bake at 375 degrees F for 40 minutes, divide into small bowls and serve cold.

Nutrition: Calories 170 Fat 5 Fiber 4 Carbs 15 Protein 11

Strawberry Buckwheat Pancakes

Preparation Time: 20 minutes

Cooking Time: 5 minutes

Servings: 4

Ingredients:

- 100g (3½oz) strawberries, chopped
- 100g (3½ oz.) buckwheat flour
- 1 egg
- 250mls (8fl oz.) milk
- 1 teaspoon olive oil
- 1 teaspoon olive oil for frying
- Freshly squeezed juice of 1 orange
- 175 calories per serving

Directions:

1. Pour the milk into a bowl and mix in the egg and a teaspoon of olive oil. Sift in the flour to the liquid mixture until smooth and creamy. Allow it to rest for 15 minutes. Heat a little oil in a pan and pour in a quarter of the mixture (or to the size you prefer.) Sprinkle in a quarter of the strawberries into the batter. Cook for around 2 minutes on

each side. Serve hot with a drizzle of orange juice. You could try experimenting with other berries such as blueberries and blackberries

Nutrition: Calories Fat Fiber Carbs Protein

Strawberry & Nut Granola

Preparation Time: 10 minutes

Cooking Time: 50 minutes

Servings: 12

Ingredients:

- 200g (7oz) oats
- 250g (9oz) buckwheat flakes
- 100g (3½ oz.) walnuts, chopped
- 100g (3½ oz.) almonds, chopped
- 100g (3½ oz.) dried strawberries
- 1½ teaspoons ground ginger
- 1½ teaspoons ground cinnamon
- 120mls (4fl oz.) olive oil
- 2 tablespoon honey

Directions:

1. Combine the oats, buckwheat flakes, nuts, ginger and cinnamon. In a saucepan, warm the oil and honey. Stir until the honey has melted. Pour the warm oil into the dry ingredients and mix well. Spread the mixture out on a large baking tray (or two) and bake in the oven at 150C (300F) for

around 50 minutes until the granola is golden. Allow it to cool. Add in the dried berries. Store in an airtight container until ready to use. Can be served with yogurt, milk or even dry as a handy snack.

Nutrition: Calories 391 Fat 0 Fiber 6 Carbs 3 Protein 8

Chilled Strawberry & Walnut Porridge

Preparation Time: 10 minutes

Cooking Time: 0 minutes

Servings: 1

Ingredients:

- 100g (3½ oz.) strawberries
- 50g (2oz) rolled oats
- 4 walnut halves, chopped
- 1 teaspoon chia seeds
- 200mls (7fl oz.) unsweetened soya milk
- 100ml (3½ FL oz.) water

Directions:

1. Place the strawberries, oats, soya milk and water into a blender and process until smooth. Stir in the chia seeds and mix well. Chill in the fridge overnight and serve in the morning with a sprinkling of chopped walnuts. It's simple and delicious.

Nutrition: Calories 384 Fat 2 Fiber 5 Carbs 3 Protein7

Fruit & Nut Yogurt Crunch

Preparation Time: 5 minutes

Cooking Time: 0 minutes

Servings: 1

Ingredients:

- 100g (3½ oz.) plain Greek yogurt
- 50g (2oz) strawberries, chopped
- 6 walnut halves, chopped
- Sprinkling of cocoa powder

Directions:

1. Stir half of the chopped strawberries into the yogurt. Using a glass, place a layer of yogurt with

a sprinkling of strawberries and walnuts, followed by another layer of the same until you reach the top of the glass. Garnish with walnuts pieces and a dusting of cocoa powder.

Nutrition: Calories 296 Fat 4 Fiber 2 Carbs 5 Protein 9

Cheesy Baked Eggs

Preparation Time: 5 minutes

Cooking Time: 15 minutes

Servings: 4

Ingredients:

- 4 large eggs
- 75g (3oz) cheese, grated
- 25g (1oz) fresh rocket (arugula) leaves, finely chopped
- 1 tablespoon parsley
- ½ teaspoon ground turmeric
- 1 tablespoon olive oil

Directions:

1. Grease each ramekin dish with a little olive oil. Divide the rocket (arugula) between the ramekin dishes then break an egg into each one. Sprinkle a little parsley and turmeric on top then sprinkle on the cheese. Place the ramekins in a preheated oven at 220C/425F for 15 minutes, until the eggs are set and the cheese is bubbling.

Nutrition: Calories 198 Fat 9 Fiber 3 Carbs 2 Protein 13

Green Egg Scramble

Preparation Time: 10 minutes

Cooking Time: 5 minutes

Servings: 1

Ingredients:

- 2 eggs, whisked
- 25g (1oz) rocket (arugula) leaves
- 1 teaspoon chives, chopped
- 1 teaspoon fresh basil, chopped
- 1 teaspoon fresh parsley, chopped
- 1 tablespoon olive oil

Directions:

1. Mix the eggs together with the rocket (arugula) and herbs. Heat the oil in a frying pan and pour into the egg mixture. Gently stir until it's lightly scrambled. Season and serve.

Nutrition: Calories 250 Fat 5 Fiber 7 Carbs 8 Protein 11

Spiced Scramble

Preparation Time: 10 minutes

Cooking Time: 5 minutes

Servings: 1

Ingredients:

- 25g (1oz) kale, finely chopped
- 2 eggs
- 1 spring onion (scallion) finely chopped
- 1 teaspoon turmeric
- 1 tablespoon olive oil
- Sea salt
- Freshly ground black pepper

Directions:

1. Crack the eggs into a bowl. Add the turmeric and whisk them. Season with salt and pepper. Heat the oil in a frying pan, add the kale and spring onions (scallions) and cook until it has wilted. Pour in the beaten eggs and stir until eggs have scrambled together with the kale.

Nutrition: Calories 259 Fat 3 Fiber 4 Carbs 3 Protein 9

Potato Bites

Preparation Time: 10 minutes

Cooking Time: 20 minutes

Servings: 3

Ingredients:

- 1 potato, sliced
- 2 bacon slices, already cooked and crumbled
- 1 small avocado, pitted and cubed
- Cooking spray

Directions:

1. Spread potato slices on a lined baking sheet, spray with cooking oil, introduce in the oven at 350 degrees F, bake for 20 minutes, arrange on a platter, top each slice with avocado and crumbled bacon and serve as a snack.

Nutrition: Calories 180 Fat 4 Fiber 1 Carbs 8 Protein 6

Eggplant Salsa

Preparation Time: 10 minutes

Cooking Time: 10 minutes

Servings: 4

Ingredients:

- 1 and ½ cups tomatoes, chopped
- 3 cups eggplant, cubed
- A drizzle of olive oil
- 2 teaspoons capers
- 6 ounces' green olives, pitted and sliced
- 4 garlic cloves, minced
- 2 teaspoons balsamic vinegar
- 1 tablespoon basil, chopped
- Black pepper to the taste

Directions:

1. Heat a saucepan with the oil medium-high heat, add eggplant, stir and cook for 5 minutes.
2. Add tomatoes, capers, olives, garlic, vinegar, basil and black pepper, toss, cook for 5 minutes more, divide into small cups and serve cold.

Nutrition: Calories 120 Fat 6 Fiber 5 Carbs 9 Protein 7

Carrots and Cauliflower Spread

Preparation Time: 10 minutes

Cooking Time: 40 minutes

Servings: 4

Ingredients:

- 1 cup carrots, sliced
- 2 cups cauliflower florets
- ½ cup cashews
- 2 and ½ cups water
- 1 cup almond milk
- 1 teaspoon garlic powder
- ¼ teaspoon smoked paprika

Directions:

1. In a small pot, mix the carrots with cauliflower, cashews and water, stir, cover, bring to a boil over medium heat, cook for 40 minutes, drain and transfer to a blender.

2. Add almond milk, garlic powder and paprika, pulse well, divide into small bowls and serve

Nutrition: Calories 201 Fat 7 Fiber 4 Carbs 7 Protein 7

Black Bean Salsa

Preparation Time: 10 minutes

Cooking Time: 0 minutes

Servings: 6

Ingredients:

- 1 tablespoon coconut aminos
- ½ teaspoon cumin, ground
- 1 cup canned black beans, no-salt-added, drained and rinsed
- 1 cup salsa
- 6 cups romaine lettuce leaves, torn
- ½ cup avocado, peeled, pitted and cubed

Directions:

1. In a bowl, combine the beans with the aminos, cumin, salsa, lettuce and avocado, toss, divide into small bowls and serve as a snack.

Nutrition: Calories 181 Fat 4 Fiber 7 Carbs 14 Protein 7

Mung Sprouts Salsa

Preparation Time: 10 minutes

Cooking Time: 0 minutes

Servings: 2

Ingredients:

- 1 red onion, chopped
- 2 cups Mung beans, sprouted
- A pinch of red chili powder
- 1 green chili pepper, chopped
- 1 tomato, chopped
- 1 teaspoon chaat masala
- 1 teaspoon lemon juice
- 1 tablespoon coriander, chopped
- Black pepper to the taste

Directions:

1. In a salad bowl, mix onion with Mung sprouts, chili pepper, tomato, chili powder, chaat masala, lemon juice, coriander and pepper, toss well, divide into small cups and serve.

Nutrition: Calories 100 Fiber 1 Fat 3 Carbs 3 Protein 6

Sprouts and Apples Snack Salad

Preparation Time: 10 minutes

Cooking Time: 0 minutes

Servings: 4

Ingredients:

- 1-pound Brussels sprouts, shredded
- 1 cup walnuts, chopped
- 1 apple, cored and cubed
- 1 red onion, chopped
- For the salad dressing:
- 3 tablespoons red vinegar
- 1 tablespoon mustard
- ½ cup olive oil
- 1 garlic clove, minced
- Black pepper to the taste

Directions:

1. In a salad bowl, mix sprouts with apple, onion and walnuts.
2. In another bowl, mix vinegar with mustard, oil, garlic and pepper, whisk really well, add this to your salad, toss well and serve as a snack.

Nutrition: Calories 120 Fat 2 Fiber 2 Carbs 8 Protein 6

Dijon Celery Salad

Preparation Time: 10 minutes

Cooking Time: 0 minutes

Servings: 4

Ingredients:

- 5 teaspoons stevia
- ½ cup lemon juice
- 1/3 cup Dijon mustard
- 2/3 cup olive oil
- Black pepper to the taste
- 2 apples, cored, peeled and cubed
- 1 bunch celery and leaves, roughly chopped
- ¾ cup walnuts, chopped

Directions:

1. In a salad bowl, mix celery and its leaves with apple pieces and walnuts.
2. Add black pepper, lemon juice, mustard, stevia and olive oil, whisk well, add to your salad, toss, divide into small cups and serve as a snack.

Nutrition: Calories 125 Fat 2 Fiber 2 Carbs 7 Protein 7

Napa Cabbage Slaw

Preparation Time: 10 minutes

Cooking Time: 0 minutes

Servings: 4

Ingredients:

- ½ cup of red bell pepper, cut into thin strips
- 1 carrot, grated
- 4 cups Napa cabbage, shredded
- 3 green onions, chopped
- 1 tablespoon olive oil
- 2 teaspoons ginger, grated
- ½ teaspoon red pepper flakes, crushed
- 3 tablespoons balsamic vinegar
- 1 tablespoon coconut aminos
- 3 tablespoons low-fat peanut butter

Directions:

1. In a salad bowl, mix bell pepper with carrot, cabbage and onions and toss.
2. Add oil, ginger, pepper flakes, vinegar, aminos and peanut butter, toss, divide into small cups and serve.

Nutrition: Calories 160 Fat 10 Fiber 3 Carbs 10 Protein 5

CONCLUSION

The things to watch out for when coming off keto are weight gain, bloating, more energy, and feeling hungry. The weight gain is nothing to freak out over; perhaps, you might not even gain any. It all depends on your diet, how your body processes carbs, and, of course, water weight. The length of your keto diet is a significant factor in how much weight you have lost, which is caused by the reduction of carbs. The bloating will occur because of the reintroduction of fibrous foods and your body getting used to digesting them again. The bloating van lasts for a few days to a few weeks. You will feel like you have more energy because carbs break down into glucose, which is the body's primary source of fuel. You may also notice better brain function and the ability to work out more.

Whether you have met your weight loss goals, your life changes, or you simply want to eat whatever you want again. You cannot just suddenly start consuming carbs again for it will shock your system. Have an idea of what you want to allow back into your consumption slowly. Be familiar with portion sizes and stick to that amount of carbs for the first few times you eat post-keto.

Start with non-processed carbs like whole grain, beans, and fruits. Start slow and see how your body responds before resolving to add carbs one meal at a time.

The ketogenic diet is the ultimate tool you can use to plan your future. Can you picture being more involved, more productive and efficient, and more relaxed and energetic? That future is possible for you, and it does not have to be a complicated process to achieve that vision. You can choose right now to be healthier and slimmer and more fulfilled tomorrow. It is possible with the ketogenic diet.

It does not just improve your physical health but your mental and emotional health as well. This diet improves your health holistically. Do not give up now as there will be quite a few days where you may think to yourself, "Why am I doing this?" and to answer that, simply focus on the goals you wish to achieve.

A good diet enriched with all the proper nutrients is our best shot of achieving an active metabolism and efficient lifestyle. A lot of people think that the Keto diet is simply for people who are interested in losing weight. You will find that it is quite the opposite. There are intense keto diets where only 5 percent of the diet comes from carbs, 20 percent is from protein, and 75 percent is from fat. But even a modified version of this which involves consciously choosing foods low in carbohydrate and high in healthy fats is good enough.

Thanks for reading this book. I hope it has provided you with enough insight to get you going. Don't put off getting started. The sooner you begin this diet, the sooner you'll start to notice an improvement in your health and well-being.